A New Class of
Singular Integral Equations and
to Differential Equations with S

Leonid Grigor'evich Mikhailov

L. G. MIKHAILOV

Physico — Technical Institute
Dušambe, the USSR

A New Class of Singular Integral Equations and its Application to Differential Equations with Singular Coefficients

translated from the Russian by

M. D. FRIEDMAN

WOLTERS-NOORDHOFF PUBLISHING GRONINGEN 1970
THE NETHERLANDS

Library of Congress Catalog Card Number 74–119884
ISBN: 90. 01. 58860. 3

Printed in Germany

CONTENTS

INTRODUCTION

The classical method of potential of a volume, simple and double layer and methods of complex-variable function theory, where Cauchy-type integrals play the part analogous to potentials, permit the reduction of boundary value problems of mathematical physics to integral equations. A boundary value problem consisting of two parts, the equation and the boundary condition, is reduced to a single integral equation which is most often completely equivalent to the original problem.

In connection with the broadening of the circle of equations and boundary conditions, new types of integral equations are obtained. Thus, after the Fredholm equations for the Dirichlet, Neumann and other problems, there appeared singular integral equations which describe different problems of plane elasticity and hydrodynamic theories well.

Many problems of mathematical physics, as for example, the Schroedinger problem in quantum mechanics, lead to partial differential equations whose coefficients have first and second order singularities. The fundamental part of this monograph is devoted to such equations, which have barely been studied up to the present, and to an associated new class of singular integral equations.

Underlying the method of integral equations is the concept of the fundamental solution, or potential, which is a function of $\frac{1}{r}$ for the Laplace equation in three-space or of $\ln\frac{1}{r}$ on a plane. Let us clarify the scheme of the method of potentials by an example which also permits an introduction to the basic circle of questions studied in chapters I, II. Using the representation $u(x)$ in terms of the volume potential and substituting into the equation

$$\Delta U + \sum_{i=1}^{n} B_i(x) \cdot U'_{x_i} + C(x) \cdot U = F(x), \tag{0.1}$$

we obtain an integral equation with operators of the form

$$H_i \varphi = \int_D \frac{B_i(x) \cdot r'_{x_i}}{r^{n-1}(x, t)} \cdot \varphi(t)\, dt, \qquad K\varphi = \int_D \frac{C(x)}{r^{n-2}(x, t)} \cdot \varphi(t)\, dt, \tag{0.2}$$

where dt is the volume element; $r(x, t)$ the distance between the points x and t.
Let $B_i(x)$, $C(x)$ have the form

$$B_i(x) = \frac{b_i(x)}{\varrho^\lambda(x)}, \qquad C(x) = \frac{c(x)}{\varrho^\mu(x)}, \tag{0.3}$$

where $\varrho(x)$ is the distance to a fixed singular point $x = 0$, say. If $\lambda < 1$, $\mu < 2$, then the kernels are integrable and the operators are completely continuous. This latter circumstance leads to the Fredholm alternative for boundary value problems. See the very general investigations of such kind carried out by Giraud in [39]. The requirements on the coefficients for which the operators $H_i\varphi, K\varphi$ remain completely continuous may be weakened by assuming singularities near $\lambda = 1$, $\mu = 2$, as, for example

$$B_i(x) = \frac{b_i(x)}{\varrho \cdot \ln^{1+\varepsilon} \varrho}, \qquad C(x) = \frac{c(x)}{\varrho^2 \cdot \ln^{1+\varepsilon} \varrho}, \qquad \varepsilon > 0. \tag{0.4}$$

Similar restrictions can also be expressed in terms of the summability of the coefficients of some power or by taking functions subject to certain summability conditions as majorants rather than (0.4). Giraud thus generalized his results in [26]. Let us present his condition on the coefficients for the case of one singularity.

Let $\omega_0(x)$ be an increasing function in $(0, a)$, $0 < a < 1$, such that $\omega_0(x) \cdot \dfrac{\ln x}{x}\, \varepsilon L(0,1)$ and the integrals

$$\omega_1(x) = \int_0^x \frac{\omega_0(t)}{t}\, dt, \qquad \omega_2(x) = \int_0^x \frac{\omega_1(t)}{t}\, dt.$$

exist. If

$$|C(x)| \leqq Q \frac{\omega_1(\varrho)}{\varrho^2} \quad \text{for} \quad n \geqq 3,$$

$$|C(x)| \leqq Q \frac{\omega_0(\varrho)}{\varrho^2} \quad \text{for} \quad n = 2$$

$$|B_i(x)| \leqq Q \frac{\omega_1(\varrho)}{\varrho}, \qquad |F(x)| \leqq Q \cdot \frac{\omega_1(\varrho)}{\varrho^n}, \tag{0.5}$$

in (0.1), then the Fredholm alternative is valid for the fundamental boundary value problems.

Methods permitting the study of equations with coefficients from $L_p(D)$, $p > 2$ have been worked out in the work of I. N. Vekua on the theory of generalized Cauchy-Riemann systems and of second order equations on a plane; see [16] and chapter III.

Recently V. K. Zakharov [27] and V. P. Glushko [23] studied generalized solutions of boundary value problems for equations similar to those of interest to us. Second and fourth order equations on a plane with conditions of type (0.4) on the coefficients or with certain special coefficients with a high order singularity were considered in [27] and general higher order equations in [23], where if all the conditions are written down as applied to our case restrictions of the type $\lambda < 1$, $\mu < 2$ are again obtained. Hence, first and second order singularities when the equation has the form

$$\varDelta U + \sum_{i=1}^{n} \frac{b_i(x)}{\varrho(x)} \cdot U'_{x_i} + \frac{c(x)}{\varrho^2(x)} \cdot U = F(x) \tag{0.6}$$

were not considered in all the mentioned works. The essentially new difficulties which occur here become manageable if it is taken into account that the integral operators (0.2) are not completely continuous in this case, see the summary of chapter I below.

We shall designate (0.6) as an equation with singular coefficients. By multiplying (0.6) by $\varrho^2(x)$ it is possible to speak of degeneration of the order to zero. A. V. Bitsadze has repeatedly stressed the importance, in principle, of studying such equations. In [8] he showed that the Fredholm character of the solvability of boundary value problems is spoiled by using the example of a system of second order equations.

Degeneration of the order has barely been studied up to now although a great number of works devoted to degenerations of various types has appeared in recent years. Following M. V. Keldysh [33], many authors have considered the degeneration of elliptic equations into parabolic on the domain boundary as well as within the domain; see [28] and the bibliography there.

As has been mentioned above the method of potentials applied to (0.6) leads to operators of the form

$$T\varphi = \frac{1}{\varrho^{\alpha}(x)} \int_D \frac{\varphi(t)\, dt}{r^{n-\alpha}(x, t)}, \tag{0.7}$$

where n is the dimension of the space and $0 < \alpha < n$. The kernel has a fixed polar singularity for $\varrho(x) = 0$ and a moving singularity for $t = x$ where the sum of the orders equals the dimension of the integral. For $t = 0$ the kernel takes the form $\dfrac{1}{\varrho^{n}(x)}$ and is not integrable in either the usual Riemann or Lebesgue sense or in the sense of the principal value.

In the one-dimensional case the kernel $\dfrac{1}{|x - c|^{\alpha}\, |t - x|^{1-\alpha}}$ seems to occupy an intermediate position between the kernels $\dfrac{1}{t - x}$ and $\dfrac{1}{x - c}$, being quite distinct, however in that the singularities are of modular type. Equations with singularities of the form $\dfrac{1}{t - x}$ form a class of singular integral equations which has been studied in detail by T. Carleman, F. Noether, N. I. Muskhelishvili, I. N. Vekua, S. G. Mikhlin, F. D. Gakhov, etc. The general theorems on the solvability of these equations, the Noether theorems, differ from the Fredholm theorems. As Fubini [76] showed, the Fredholm theorems are valid for equations with kernels of $\dfrac{1}{x - c}$ type although the integral is indeed understood in the sense of the principal value.

Integral operators of the type (0.7) and corresponding equations of the second kind are studied in chapter I. This material is the basis of the method applied in chapters II and III. It seems that the customary spaces of type C or L_p are transformed by the operator $T\varphi$ into broader spaces, i.e., the operator itself is not a bounded operator in C and L_p. Spaces constructed according to the following simple scheme (not used up to now insofar as we know) seem natural: we divide the functions of class C by $\varrho^\beta(x)$, $\beta > 0$. We denote the obtained class, evidently broader and at the same time equivalent to C by C_β. If $f(x) \in C_\beta$, then $f(x) = \dfrac{f_0(x)}{\varrho^\beta(x)}$, where $f_0(x) \in C$. We put $\|f\|_{C_\beta} = \|f_0\|_C$ so that C_β is isometric to C. Using the factor $\varrho^\beta(x)$ it is possible to carry out isometric transformations of other classes of functions S (bounded, measurable), H, C^m etc., which leads to the classes S_β, H_β, C^m_β etc. In place of the single singular point it is possible to consider the singular subset F and to carry out analogous transformations by replacing $\varrho(x)$ by $\pi(x)$, the distance to F, as is done in section 1. The mentioned scheme of "distortion" of the properties of the functions in a certain subset may be developed and used very broadly, as chapters I—III indicate.

The operator $T\varphi$ is bounded in the spaces S_β, C_β, etc. We find the exact value of its norm which does not seem to depend on the shape and size of the domain but only on the location of the singular points relative to the domain, namely, on whether it is an interior or boundary point, and in the latter case, a smoothness or conical point, etc. The operator $T\varphi$ is not completely continuous. This important circumstance is explained roughly by the fact that an isometric mapping of the function occurs at the singular point which is expressed, say, in the relation $\omega(0) = q\Phi(0)$, where $\Phi(x) = \varrho^\beta(x) \cdot \varphi(x)$, $\omega(x) = \varrho^\beta(x) \cdot T\varphi$, and q is a completely defined number independent of $\Phi(x)$ and of the domain.

We shall also consider operators with several singular points, with a singular hyperplane and with several such hyperplanes. For the general operator

$$K\varphi = \frac{1}{\varrho^\alpha(x)} \int\limits_D \frac{K(x, t)}{r^{n-\alpha}(x, t)} \cdot \varphi(t)\, dt,$$

which is linear in the same spaces as is $T\varphi$, necessary and sufficient conditions for the complete continuity will be given.

Transforming to integral equations, we will formulate the existence and uniqueness theorem and we will derive the condition under which the Fredholm theorems are valid; it consists of the smallness of $K(x, t)$ in a singular manifold.

The theory of this class of integral equations is not completely closed since there are no general theorems of Fredholm and Noether type without some restrictions on the smallness of the kernel. The reason is, possibly, that so very broad a class of equations is included. If singular integral equations are taken, say, one theory is known in the one-dimensional case and another in the multi-dimensional case. Hence, we will study certain particular types of equations in greater detail: Volterra type equations and equations in all of space. Complex equations on a plane from chapter III section 4 also border on these.

The singular, non-Fredholmian character of the considered equations is explained by such facts as the continuous spectrum, the difference in the solvability of the given and the transpose equations, the violation of the Fredholm alternative, etc. Chapter I is of independent value and, it is understood, its applications are not exhausted by those considered in chapters II and III. Thus, the mentioned Volterra-type equations have a close connection with problems of the axisymmetric theory of elasticity [1].

Chapter II is devoted to the equations (0.6). The general properties of the equations are studied here and the boundary value problems are investigated. Among the first group of questions are the investigation of the maximum principle and the manifold of solutions. Because of the presence of the singularity in the coefficients, the structure of the solutions, their zeroes and singularities is spoiled, for example, the concept of a fundamental solution loses meaning, etc. Hence, questions of the existence of solutions which are continuous at the singular point, bounded or with a polar singularity are studied first. Equation (0.6) is similar to equations of the Fuks class in the analytic theory of ordinary differential equations. By analogy, we will consider equations with one, two and more singular points as well as with singular manifolds and also equations in the whole space. All the fundamental boundary value problems, with the exception of the problem with a skew derivative will be solved by a single method, by reducing them to integral equations studied

and mechanical problems for surfaces and shells with singular points is pointed out.

Chapters I, II, III form a single whole, chapter IV differs somewhat from the preceding in its direction. It is devoted to the general boundary value problem of conjugate analytic functions

$$\varphi^+(t) = a(t) \cdot \varphi^-(t) + b(t) \cdot \overline{\varphi^-(t)} + c(t), \qquad \varphi^-(\infty) = 0, \qquad \text{(A)}$$

and to various applications.

The problem was posed by A. I. Markushevich in 1946 and he investigated it for $a \equiv c \equiv 0$, $b \equiv 1$. In 1952 N. P. Vekua reduced it to a singular integral equation, obtained the condition for normal solvability $a(t) \neq 0$ and proved its solvability in the class of meromorphic functions, which concerns the class of holomorphic functions, then there were only the alternative statements of the Noether theorem type. The problem (A) became important in the work of I. N. Vekua [16] on the flexures of glued surfaces. In this connection, B. V. Boiarskii investigated it in 1959, see [11] and [16], p. 456. By indicating the essential value of the condition $|a(t)| > |b(t)|$ he obtained the first exact results for this case. Considering the conjugate problem (A*) and following N. P. Vekua, he proved the Noether theorems for the boundary value problems (A) and (A*). Reducing them to ordinary singular integral equations, he used representations of Cauchy type integrals with real density. Such a representation is very awkward in the multiconnected domain case, hence, it is not accident that he limits himself to simply-connected domains. His method of investigating the homogeneous problem consists of simplifying the boundary condition to the continuity condition because of the complexity of the desired function; it is the solution of the Beltrami system. Because of such awkwardness of the method, the Hölder condition with exponent as close as desired to unity must be imposed on $a(t)$.

In substance, chapter IV contains a complete theory of the problem (A) under very general conditions: $a(t)$ continuous, $b(t)$ measurable and bounded $c(t) \in L_p$, $p > 1$.

It is no less important that the results have been obtained by several different methods which are completely natural and, probably, the simplest possible in the given problem. The problem

(A) has been studied at that level at which the well-known Riemann and Hilbert boundary value problems are found [20, 60, 77]. Let us also note that we obtained the first fundamental results at the beginning of 1960 and announced them in September 1960 to the Fifth All-Union Conference on Complex-Variable Function Theory (see the abstracts of reports, Erevan, 1960). The above-mentioned work of B. V. Boiarskii [11] was published at the beginning of 1961.

The cases

$$1.\ |a(t)| > |b(t)|, \quad 2.\ |a(t)| \equiv |b(t)|, \quad 3.\ |a(t)| < |b(t)|,$$

which we designate, respectively, as elliptic, parabolic and hyperbolic, should be differentiated in the problem (A). As is shown in sections 1—4, the problem (A) with $|a(t)| > |b(t)|$ is qualitatively equivalent to the particular case $b \equiv 0$, i.e., to the Riemann problem first studied in general form by F. D. Gakhov [20], with the exception, however, that it is not elementary in nature. The method of successive approximations of the solution to problem (A) which may also be used for its numerical computation is worked out in section 1. Certain other problems are also solved by this method: The problem (A) for open contours or with discontinuous coefficients; the problem with derivatives in the boundary conditions; nonlinear problems. A direct qualitative investigation of the homogeneous problem is very simple.

Another method of investigating the problem (A) is to reduce it to integral equations by using the Noether theorem and a qualitative investigation of the homogeneous problem. For the problem (A) such an integral equation is

$$\alpha_1\mu + \beta_1 \cdot S\mu + \alpha_2\overline{\mu} + \beta_2 \cdot \overline{S\mu} = \gamma, \tag{0.11}$$

where

$$S\mu = \frac{1}{\pi i}\int_{\Gamma} \frac{\mu(\tau)}{\tau - t}\,d\tau. \tag{0.12}$$

In this connection we will construct a general theory of the integral equations

$$\alpha_1\mu + \beta_1 S\mu + \alpha_2\overline{\mu} + \beta_2\overline{S\mu} + K_1\mu + \overline{K_2\mu} = \gamma, \tag{0.13}$$

(where K_1, K_2 are completely continuous operators), which is undoubtedly also of independent interest.

Completely new is the investigation of the parabolic case $|a(t)| \equiv |b(t)|$. The problem is decomposed into two related problems of the type

$$\varphi^+ = G\overline{\varphi^+} + g. \tag{B}$$

In the case of a simply connected domain (B) reduces to the Riemann problem in certain other cases to the Hilbert problem, but in the general case of a multiply connected domain it is new and not yet studied, however, see [69].

The results obtained for the boundary value problem (A), are used in section 5 to obtain exact theorems on the solvability of the integral equation (0.11), which here plays the part of analog of the well-known characteristic singular integral equation [20] and which includes a whole set of different equations, both singular and Fredholmian, complex and real. The integral equations of the plane theory of potentials, which are themselves of great importance, reduce to it.

Conjugate problems, similar to the Riemann problem in the theory of analytic functions, acquire value together with the internal and external boundary value problems in mathematical physics. In 1954—55 the author considered a Riemann-type problem for the generalized Cauchy-Riemann system. The more general problem of type (A) is investigated for this system in section 6 and the problem of conjugate solutions of a second order differential equation in section 7.

The store of such problems for second order partial differential equations is as yet quite small. S. M. Nikol'skii considered the problem of conjugate harmonic functions with the condition of a finite Dirichlet integral and certain others [63]. O. A. Oleinik [66] investigated the Dirichlet problem for equations with discontinuous coefficients and conditions of conjugate normal derivatives on the lines of discontinuity. The solution exists and is unique in the mentioned problems. The problems we consider in section 7 differ in that they may have a non-unique solution or may require solvability conditions which, in brief, have an index $\varkappa$.

The monograph is a summary of the author's researches between 1956—62. Many results, particularly in chapter I, are published for the first time. On the other hand, various questions, particularly in chapter III, are expounded fragmentarily.

Details may be found in the following publications: for chapter I in [49, 41, 44]; for chapter II in [48, 56, 55]; for chapter III in [42, 43, 46, 47]; for chapter IV in [45, 50—53].

A good conception of the scope of the research is given by the detailed table of contents.

Chapter I

NEW CLASS OF SINGULAR INTEGRAL EQUATIONS

1. Certain Classes of Functions

1.1. Notation. The following notation is used throughout: E is an n dimensional Euclidean space of the points $x = (x_1, \ldots, x_n)$, D is a finite domain, $f(x) = f(x_1, \ldots, x_n)$, $dx = dx_1, \ldots, dx_n$, $\int_D f(x)dx$ is a multiple integral in the domain D,
$r(x, t) = \sqrt{\sum_1^n (x_i - t_i)^2}$ is the distance between the points x and t,
$\varrho(x) = r(x, 0)$ is the distance to the origin,
$S(D)$ is a class of bounded measurable functions with the norm

$$\|f\|_{S(D)} = \operatorname*{Sup}_{x \in D} |f(x)| .$$

The Sup and inf are understood to be the essential exact boundaries, i.e., without taking account of sets of measure zero. The class $S(D)$ is a complete linear, normalized space, i.e., Banach space.
$C(D)$ is a class of continuous functions with the norm

$$\|f\|_C = \max_{x \in D} |f(x)| .$$

$C^m(D)$ is a class of m tuply continuously differentiable functions with the norm

$$\|f\|_{C^m(D)} = \sum_{K=0}^{m} \sum_{K_1+K_2+\ldots+K_n=K} \max_D \left| \frac{\partial^k f}{\partial x_1^{K_1} \partial x_2^{K_2} \ldots \partial x_n^{K_n}} \right| ,$$

$H(D)$ is a class of functions satisfying the Hölder condition

$$|f(x) - f(t)| \leq M(f) \cdot r^\lambda(x, t) \quad \text{for all } x,\ t \in D .$$

We shall sometimes mention an exponent of the class λ and we shall write $H(D) \equiv H(\lambda, D)$. The norm in $H(\lambda, D)$ is introduced by means of the formula

$$\|f\|_{H(D)} = \|f\|_C + \sup_{x,t\in D} \frac{|f(x) - f(t)|}{r^\lambda(x, t)}.$$

The second member is, in fact, the least of the Hölder constants. For brevity, we shall write $\|f\|_{h(\lambda, D)}$ instead. All these classes also generate a Banach space.

We shall consider various unbounded domains as, say, the whole space E or the complement of the finite domain D in E, which will be denoted by D^-.

Under the same definitions of the norm we obtain the Banach spaces $S(E)$, $C(E)$, $H(E)$ etc. Let us note that the requirement $f(x) \in H(\lambda, E)$ means that $|f(x) - f(\infty)| \leqq M \cdot \varrho^{-\lambda}(x)$ for $\varrho(x) \to \infty$ and that, as before, $\|f\|_{H(\lambda, E)} = \|f\|_C + \sup_{x,t\in E} M(f)$, where $M(f)$ is defined as $\sup_{x\in E} \varrho^\lambda(x) \cdot |f(x) - f(\infty)|$ for $x = \infty$.

1.2. Classes of Functions with Isolated Subsets. Let $0 \in D$. We shall call the function $f(x)$ continuous at the point $x = 0$, if the inequality $|f(x) - f(0)| < \varepsilon$ is satisfied for $\varrho(x) < \delta$ for almost all x. Let C_0S be the class of functions $f(x) \in S(D)$ which are continuous at the point $x = 0$ and with the same norm as in S.

H_0S the class of functions $f(x) \in S(D)$ which satisfy the Hölder condition at the point $x = 0$, i.e., for $\varrho(x) \to 0$ and for almost all x there is compliance with the inequality

$$|f(x) - f(0)| \leqq M \cdot \varrho^\lambda(x), \qquad \lambda > 0.$$

The condition $\lambda \leqq 1$ is not assumed here. The norm in H_0S is introduced by means of the formula

$$\|f\|_{H_0S} = \|f\|_S + \sup_{x\in D} \frac{|f(x) - f(0)|}{\varrho^\lambda(x)} \tag{1.1}$$

The second member is actually the least of the Hölder constants. For brevity, we shall also write $\|f\|_{h(\lambda, 0)}$ instead.

H_0C the class of functions which are continuous in the domain and satisfy the Hölder condition at the point $x = 0$ with the norm (1.1).

Let us show that all these classes generate a Banach space. The axioms of the norm are verified easily; let us prove the completeness.

Completeness of C_0S. Let a fundamental sequence be given in C_0S, i.e., the inequality

$$\| f_n - f_m \|_{C_0S} = \| f_n(x) - f_m(x) \|_S < \varepsilon \tag{1.2}$$

holds for all $n, m > N(\varepsilon)$ and almost all $x \in D$. Hence, it follows because of the completeness of S, that $f_n(x)$ converges almost everywhere to a certain bounded function $f(x)$. Passing to the limit in (1.2) as $x \to 0$, we obtain $|f_n(0 - f_m(0)| < \varepsilon$, from which the convergence of $\{f_n(0)\}$ follows. Putting $f(0) = \lim_{n\to\infty} f_n(0)$, we will have the function $f(x)$, continuous at the point 0.

In fact, we have $|f(x) - f_n(x)| < \frac{\varepsilon}{3}$ in the inequality

$$|f(x) - f(0)| \leqq |f(x) - f_n(x)| + |f_n(x) - f_n(0)| + |f_n(0) - f(0)|$$

for almost all x for $\varrho(x) < \delta$ because of the convergence in $S(D)$, $|f_n(x) - f_n(0)| < \frac{\varepsilon}{3}$ because of the continuity of $f_n(x)$ and $|f_n(0) - f(0)| < \frac{\varepsilon}{3}$ for $n > N(\varepsilon)$. Hence, $|f(x) - f(0)| < \varepsilon$ for $\varrho(x) < \delta$ for almost all x. The statement is proved.

Completeness of H_0S. Let fundamentality be given in $H_0S(D)$

$$\| \varphi_n(x) - \varphi_m(x) \|_{H_0S} < \varepsilon. \tag{1.3}$$

Fundamentality in C_0S and S, thereby follows so that $\{\varphi_n(x)\}$ converges almost everywhere to $\varphi(x) \in S(D)$ and $\varphi(x)$ is continuous for $x = 0$. From (1.3) we also have

$$\operatorname*{Sup}_{x\in D} \frac{|[\varphi_n(x) - \varphi_m(x)] - [\varphi_n(0) - \varphi_m(0)]|}{\varrho^\lambda(x)} < \varepsilon \tag{1.4}$$

for all $n, m > N$. Here letting $m \to \infty$, we obtain

$$\operatorname*{Sup}_{x\in D} \frac{|[\varphi_n(x) - \varphi(x)] - [\varphi_n(0) - \varphi(0)]|}{\varrho^\lambda(x)} \leqq \varepsilon. \tag{1.5}$$

Denoting the Hölder constants of the functions $\varphi_n(x)$ and $\varphi(x)$ by M_n and M, we may write

$$|M_n - M| = \left| \operatorname*{Sup}_{x \in D} \frac{|\varphi_n(x) - \varphi_n(0)|}{\varrho^\lambda(x)} - \operatorname*{Sup}_{x \in D} \frac{|\varphi(x) - \varphi(0)|}{\varrho^\lambda(x)} \right|$$

$$\leqq \operatorname{Sup} \left| \frac{|\varphi_n(x) - \varphi_n(0)|}{\varrho^\lambda(x)} - \frac{|\varphi(x) - \varphi(0)|}{\varrho^\lambda(x)} \right| \leqq \varepsilon,$$

i.e., $|M_n - M| < \varepsilon$, or $M_n \to M$. It is hence clear that $\{\varphi_n(x)\}$ converges in the sense of $H_0 S$ and $\varphi(x) \in H_0 S$.

Completeness of $H_0 C$ is proved in exactly the same manner.

Classes of functions with the isolation of several points of continuity or H-continuity are introduced analogously. Lines and, in general, any subsets of different dimensionality can also take the part of such exclusive sets. Let F be an arbitrary closed set and $F < \bar{D}$. Let $C(F)\,S(D)$ denote functions from $S(D)$ continuous in F, and $H(F)\,S(D)$ functions satisfying the Hölder condition in F etc. The norm in $C(F)\,S(D)$ agrees with the norm in $S(D)$, and is given in $H(F)\,S(D)$ by the formula

$$\|f\|_{H(F)S(D)} = \|f\|_{S(D)} + \operatorname*{Sup}_{\substack{x_1 \in D \\ x_2 \in F}} \frac{|f(x_1) - f(x_2)|}{r^\lambda(x_1, x_2)}$$

All the introduced classes generate complete spaces. This is proved by exactly the same scheme as above.

If fundamentality is given in $H(F)\,S(D)$, then fundamentality in $H_a S(D)$ follows for each point $a \in F$. As has been proved above, convergence at the point a follows and $f(x) \in H_a\, S(D)$. By letting the point a run through the whole set F, we obtain the statement above.

1.3. Classes of Functions with Singularities. Let the point 0 lie in D. Let us introduce the new class $S_\beta(D)$ or $S(\beta, D)$ of functions representable in the form

$$f(x) = \varrho^{-\beta}(x) \cdot f_0(x), \qquad \text{where } f_0(x) \in S(D).$$

If $\beta > 0$, then $f(x)$ generally has a polar singularity at the point 0. Roughly speaking, the class $S(\beta, D)$ is obtained if all functions $S(D)$ are divided by $\varrho^\beta(x)$.

Let us introduce the norm

$$\|f\|_{S(\beta,D)} = \operatorname*{Sup}_{x \in D} \varrho^{\beta}(x) \cdot |f(x)|,$$

i.e. $\|f\|_{S(\beta,D)} = \|f_0\|_{S(D)}$. The class $S(\beta, D)$ is isometric to $S(D)$ and includes it. Henceforth, we shall consider $S(\beta, D)$ mainly for $\beta > 0$. The properties of functions of this class will be somewhat different for the exterior domain. Functions of the class $S(\beta, D^-)$, $\beta > 0$ vanish at infinity and $S(\beta, D^-) < S(D^-)$, and functions of the class $S(\beta, E)$, $\beta > 0$, vanish at infinity and have a singularity at $x = 0$.

Isometric transformations of other classes of functions may be carried out by using the factor $\varrho^{-\beta}(x)$. Transformation of the classes $C(D)$, $C^m(D)$, $H(\lambda, D)$ leads to the classes $C_\beta(D)$, $C^m_\beta(D)$, $H_\beta(\lambda, D)$. The function $f(x) = f_0(x) \cdot \varrho^{-\beta}(x)$ belongs to the class $C_\beta(D)$, $C^m_\beta(D)$ or $H_\beta(\lambda, D)$, if $f_0(x)$ belongs to the class $C(D)$, $C^m(D)$ or $H(\lambda, D)$, respectively. Functions of the classes $C_\beta(D^-)$, $C^m_\beta(D^-)$ and $H_\beta(\lambda, D^-)$ will vanish at infinity, hence the imbeddings

$$C_\beta(D^-) < C(D^-), \quad C^m_\beta(D^-) < C^m(D^-), \quad H_\beta(D^-) < H(D^-)$$

will be performed. Isometric transformations of the classes C_0S, H_0S etc. lead to the Banach spaces $C_0S(\beta, D)$, $H_0S(\beta, D)$. For example, $f(x) \in C_0S(\beta, D)$ means that $f(x) = \varrho^{-\beta}(x) \cdot f_0(x)$, where $f_0(x) \in S(D)$ and is continuous at the point $x = 0$.

Let us now generalize our constructions with respect to isolatable singular manifolds (see the end of section 2). Let there be two singular points c_1, $c_2 \in D$, and let the domain D be finite. We will consider classes of functions $S(\beta_1, \beta_2, D)$, having polar singularities of orders β_1 and β_2 at the points c_1 and c_2. They may be transformed in Banach spaces by three methods:

First. $S(\beta_1, \beta_2, D)$ is a class of functions of the form $\varrho_1^{-\beta_1}(x) \times \varrho_2^{-\beta_2}(x) \cdot f_0(x)$, where $f_0(x) \in S(D)$ and $\varrho_1(x) = r(x, c_1)$, $\varrho_2(x) = r(x, c_2)$, with the norm

$$\|f\|_{S(\beta_1, \beta_2, D)} = \operatorname*{Sup}_{D} \varrho_1^{\beta_1}(x) \varrho_2^{\beta_2}(x) \, |f(x)|.$$

Second. Let the domain D be divided into two, D_1 and D_2, each containing one singular point $c_1 \in D_1$ and $c_2 \in D_2$. Then $f(x)$

$\in S(\beta_1, \beta_2, D)$, if $f \in S(\beta_1, D_1)$ and $f \in S(\beta_2, D_2)$; let us put

$$\|f\|_{S(\beta_1, \beta_2, D)} = \|f\|_{S(\beta_1, D_1)} + \|f\|_{S(\beta_2, D_2)}.$$

Third. Let us introduce the distance between x and the two points c_1, c_2

$$\Pi(x) = r(x, \{c_1, c_2\}).$$

If $f(x) = \Pi^{-\beta}(x) \cdot f_0(x)$, then we put $f(x) \in S(\beta, \Pi, D)$, where $f_0(x) \in S(D)$.
If $\beta = \max(\beta_1, \beta_2)$, then the class $S(\beta, \Pi, D)$ contains $S(\beta_1 \beta_2 D)$, but is somewhat broader. It levels out the differences in the orders of the singularities.
We will often have to deal with the two singular points 0 and ∞, i.e., to consider functions given in the whole space. The point $x = \infty$ has special characteristics. Three normalization methods may also be considered here:

First. $\|f\|_{S(\beta_1, \beta_2, E)} = \sup\limits_{E} \varrho_1^{\beta_1}(x) \cdot \varrho_2^{\beta_2}(x) \, |f(x)|.$

Second. Let E_1 be the sphere $\varrho(x) \leqq 1$ and $E_1^- = E - E_1$.

Let us put

$$\|f\|_{S(\beta_1, \beta_2, E)} = \|f\|_{S(\beta_1, E_1)} + \|f\|_{S(\beta_2, E_1^-)}.$$

Third. $S(\beta, E)$ is considered above; in fact, it is a particular case of the first for $\beta_1 = \beta_2$. For $\beta > 0$ functions of this class vanish at infinity and have a singularity at the point $x = 0$. Functions of the class $S(\beta_1, \beta_2, E)$ have the order β_1 at the point $x = 0$ and the order β_2 at $x = \infty$, i.e., $f(x) = 0(\varrho^{-\beta_1})$, $\varrho \to 0$, and $f(x) = 0(\varrho^{-\beta_2})$, $\varrho \to \infty$. Each of the numbers β_1, β_2 may independently be considered >0, $=0$, <0. Let the closed set $F < \overline{D}$ and let $\pi(x) = r(x, F)$. Let $S(\beta, F, D)$ or $S(\beta, \pi, D)$ denote a class of functions of the form $f(x) = \pi^{-\beta}(x) \cdot f_0(x)$, where $f_0 \in S(D)$. If $f_0(x) \in C(F)S(D)$ or $H(F)S(D)$, $C(D)$, $H(D)$ etc., then correspondingly

$$f(x) \in C(F)S(\beta, D),\ H(F)S(\beta, D),\ C(\beta, F, D),\ H(\beta, F, D) \text{ etc.}$$

and

$$\|f\|_{C(F)S(\beta, D)} = \|f_0\|_{C(F)S(D)}, \quad \|f\|_{H(F)S(\beta, D)} = \|f_0\|_{H(F)S(D)}$$

For concreteness, let us note that if $f \in S(\beta, F, D)$, then the highest possible order of the singularities at the points of F is β. Finally, it may happen that $f_0(x) \equiv 0$ on all F or on parts of it so that $f(x)$ will have a lower order singularity. Hence, the introduction of superfluously broad sets F adds no complications.

2. Properties of Some Integrals

2.1. Investigation of the Integral $\int\limits_{Ш_R} \varrho^{-\beta}(y) r^{\alpha-n}(y, I)\, dy$.

Let $Ш_R \equiv Ш(R, 0)$ be a sphere $\varrho(x) \leq R$ and let

$$q(R) \equiv q(Ш_R, \alpha, \beta) = \int\limits_{Ш_R} \varrho^{-\beta}(y) r^{\alpha-n}(y, I)\, dy, \tag{2.1}$$

where $0 < \alpha < \beta < n$, I is a point with coordinates $(1, 0, \ldots, 0)$.

Lemma 2.1. The function $q(R)$ is defined and continuous for all R, $0 \leq R \leq \infty$, increases monotonely from $q(0) = 0$ to $q(\infty) = q(\alpha, \beta)$, where

$$q(\alpha, \beta) = \int\limits_E \varrho^{-\beta}(y) \cdot r^{\alpha-n}(y, I)\, dy. \tag{2.2}$$

Moreover, $q(R) \in C^1$ for all R, $R \neq 0, 1, \infty$ and satisfies the Hölder condition with exponent λ, where $\lambda = n - \beta$ for the point $R = 0$, $\lambda = \beta - \alpha$ for $R = \infty$; $\lambda = \alpha$ for the point $R = 1$ with $\alpha < 1$, $\lambda = 1 - \varepsilon$, where $\varepsilon > 0$ is as small a number as desired, for $\alpha = 1$, and $q(R) \in C^1$ for $\alpha > 1$.

Proof.
1. Transforming to polar coordinates and taking into account that $dy = \varrho^{n-1}\, d\sigma\, d\varrho$, where $d\sigma$ is the element of area of a unit sphere σ, we will have

$$q(R) = \int\limits_\sigma d\sigma \int\limits_0^R \frac{\varrho^{n-\beta-1}}{r^{n-\alpha}(y, I)}\, d\varrho$$

$$= \int\limits_\sigma d\sigma \int\limits_0^R \frac{\varrho^{n-\beta-1}\, d\varrho}{[\varrho^2(y) - 2\varrho(y) \cos \varphi_1 + 1]^{\frac{n-\alpha}{2}}}.$$

Differentiating with respect to R under the integral sign, we obtain

$$q'(R) = R^{n-\beta-1} \int_\sigma \frac{d\sigma}{(R^2 - 2R\cos\varphi_1 + 1)^{\frac{n-a}{2}}} \tag{2.3}$$

If $R \neq 1$, then $R^2 - 2R\cos\varphi_1 + 1 = (R - \cos\varphi_1)^2 + \sin^2\varphi_1 \neq 0$, so that the integral exists and yields a continuous function of R, in which

$$\lim_{R\to 0} \int_\sigma = \omega_n, \qquad \lim_{R\to\infty} R^{n-\alpha} \int_\sigma = \omega_n,$$

where ω_n is the area of σ. Hence, $q'(R)$ is continuous for $R \neq 0, 1, \infty$ and

$$|q'(R)| \leqq (\omega_n + \varepsilon) \cdot R^{n-\beta-1} \quad \text{for} \quad R \to 0;$$

$$|q'(R)| \leqq (\omega_n + \varepsilon) \cdot \left(\frac{1}{R}\right)^{\beta-\alpha+1} \quad \text{for} \quad R \to \infty;$$

here $\varepsilon = \varepsilon(R) \to 0$. Restoring $q(R)$, we obtain

$$|q(R)| \leqq \frac{(\omega_n + \varepsilon)}{n - \beta} R^{n-\beta} \quad \text{for} \quad R \to 0,$$

$$|q(R) - q(\infty)| \leqq \frac{(\omega_n + \varepsilon)}{\beta - \alpha} \left(\frac{1}{R}\right)^{\beta-\alpha} \quad \text{for} \quad R \to \infty.$$

Remark. These two inequalities may be obtained directly from the original expression for $q(R)$. If $R \to 0$, then $\max\limits_{\varrho(y)\leqq R} r^{\alpha-n}(y, I) = C(R) \to 1$, so that

$$q(R) \leqq C(R) \cdot \int_{III_R} \varrho^{-\beta}(y)\, dy \leqq C(R) \frac{R^{n-\beta}}{n - \beta} \cdot \omega_n.$$

If $R \to \infty$, then $\max\limits_{\varrho(y)\leqq R} \left(\dfrac{r(y, I)}{\varrho(y)}\right)^{\alpha-n} = C_1(R) \to 1$ and

$$q(\infty) - q(R) \leqq C_1(R) \cdot \int_{\varrho(y)\leqq R} \varrho^{\alpha-\beta-n}(y)\, dy \leqq C_1(R) \int_\sigma d\sigma \int_R^\infty \varrho^{\alpha-\beta-1} d\varrho$$

$$= C_1(R)\, \omega_n \cdot \left(\frac{1}{R}\right)^{\beta-\alpha}, \quad \beta - \alpha > 0.$$

2. Now let $R \to 1$.
If $\alpha > 1$, then the integral in (2.3) converges uniformly for all R, including $R = 1$, and is continuous. Hence, in this case $q'(R)$ is continuous and $q(R) \in C^1$. Let us turn to the case of $\alpha < 1$. For definiteness, let us assume that $R \leqq 1$.
From the original expression for $q(R)$ we have

$$|q(R) - q(1)| = \int\limits_{R \leqq \varrho(y) \leqq 1} \varrho^{-\beta}(y) r^{\alpha-n}(y, I)\, dy \leqq C \cdot \int\limits_{R \leqq \varrho(y) \leqq 1} r^{\alpha-n}(y, I)\, dy$$

since $\varrho^{-\beta}(y)$ is bounded for $R \to 1$. Let us make the translation $y_1 - 1 = u_1$, $y_j = u_j$, $j = \overline{2, n}$ and let us transform to polar coordinates [75]. Then we will have: $\frac{\pi}{2} \leqq \varphi_1 \leqq \frac{3\pi}{2}$ and the new limits of integration in $\varrho(u)$ will be

$$\varrho_2 = \sqrt{R^2 - 2R\cos\varphi_1 + 1} \quad \text{and} \quad \varrho_1 = \sqrt{2 - 2\cos\varphi_1}$$
$$= \pm 2\sin\frac{\varphi_1}{2}.$$

Thus

$$|q(R) - q(1)| \leqq C \int\limits_{\varrho_1 \leqq \varrho(u) \leqq \varrho_2} \varrho^{\alpha-n}(u)\, du = C \int\limits_{\sigma} d\sigma \int\limits_{\varrho_1}^{\varrho_2} \varrho^{\alpha-1}\, d\varrho$$
$$= \frac{C}{\alpha} \int\limits_{\sigma} d\sigma\, (\varrho_2^\alpha - \varrho_1^\alpha) \leqq C_1 \int\limits_{\sigma} (\varrho_2 - \varrho_1)^\alpha\, d\sigma,$$

because $\varrho_2^\alpha - \varrho_1^\alpha \leqq \text{const}\,(\varrho_2 - \varrho_1)^\alpha$ for $\alpha \leqq 1$. Splitting the integral with respect to σ into multiple integrals, we obtain

$$|q(R) - q(1)| \leqq M \cdot \int\limits_0^\pi \Big[\sqrt{R^2 - 2R\cos\varphi_1 + 1}$$
$$- \sqrt{2 - 2\cos\varphi_1}\Big]^{\frac{\alpha}{2}}\, d\varphi_1$$

or

$$|q(R) - q(1)| \leqq M_1 \cdot (R^2 - 1)^\alpha$$

$$\times \int\limits_0^\pi \frac{d\varphi_1}{\left(\sqrt{R^2 - 2R\cos\varphi_1 + 1} + \sqrt{2 - 2\cos\varphi_1}\right)^\alpha}.$$

If $\alpha < 1$, the integral exists for all R including $R = 1$, so that we obtain

$$|q(R) - q(1)| \leqq C \cdot |R - 1|^{\alpha}.$$

If $\alpha = 1$, a divergent integral is obtained for the value $R = 1$. Because $r^{1-n}(y, I) \leqq r^{1-\varepsilon-n}(y, I)$, where $\varepsilon > 0$ is arbitrary, we may include the case $\alpha = 1$ in any of the preceding cases. The lemma is proved.

Let us perform an inversion relative to the unit sphere in the integral of $q(\alpha, \beta)$ (see section 1, chapter II): $y_i = -\dfrac{z_i}{\varrho^2(z)}$, $i = 1, \ldots, n$. Then the Jacobian is $|I| = \varrho^{-2n}(z)$; and $r^2(y, I) = \varrho^2(y) - 2\varrho \cos\varphi + 1$ transforms into $\varrho^2(z) \cdot r^2(z, I)$, so that

$$q(\alpha, \beta) = \int_E \frac{\varrho^{\beta}(z)\, dz}{\varrho^{2n}(z)\, \varrho^{-(n-\alpha)}(z) \cdot r^{n-\alpha}(z, I)} = \int_E \frac{dz}{\varrho^{n+\alpha-\beta}(z) \cdot r^{n-\alpha}(z, I)},$$

that is, $q(\alpha, \beta) \equiv q(\alpha, n + \alpha - \beta)$, $\alpha < \beta < n$.

This formula shows the symmetry of $q(\alpha, \beta)$ relative to the middle of its segment of definition in the variable β. Hence, it follows in particular, that the minimum is achieved precisely at the middle of the segment $\beta = \dfrac{n + \alpha}{2}$.

Let us note that $q(\alpha, \beta)$ as a function of the variables α, β is infinitely differentiable and convex, i.e., in the variable β, say:

$$q\left(\frac{\beta_1 + \beta_2}{2}\right) \leqq \frac{1}{2}[q(\beta_1) + q(\beta_2)].$$

Analogously in the variable α. It hence follows that $q(\beta)$ has a unique minimum and $q(\beta) \to \infty$ as $\beta \to \alpha$ and $\beta \to n$.

An analogous conclusion is valid for $q(R, \alpha, \beta)$.

The portion of space described by the inequalities $\varphi_k^0 \leqq \varphi_k \leqq \varphi_k^1$, $k = \overline{1, n-1}$, $0 \leqq \varrho \leqq \infty$, where $\varphi_1, \ldots, \varphi_{n-1}$ are polar angles, is designated by the cone K. We also designate the portion of space for which φ_k^0, φ_k^1, $k = 0, 1, \ldots, n$ are not constant but mutually dependent, as a cone. The truncated cone K_R is different in that $0 \leqq \varrho \leqq R$. Henceforth, we shall consider the function

$$q_k(R) \equiv q(K_R, \alpha, \beta) = \int\limits_{K_R} \varrho^{-\beta}(y)\, r^{\alpha-n}(y, I)\, dy,$$

where, as before, $I(1, 0, \ldots, 0)$, but perhaps $I \in K_R$ and $I \bar{\in} K_R$. It is easy to see that Lemma 2.1 and its proof, as well as the last remark on the nature of the dependence on the parameters α, β, are completely valid for $q_k(R)$.

Let us clarify whether the quantity $q_k(R)$ depends on the position of the cone K in space. Let the cone K_R be regarded as a solid with one fixed point. If the integral $q_k(R)$ is written as a multiple integral

$$q(K_R) = \int\limits_{\varphi_1^{(0)}}^{\varphi_1^{(1)}} d\varphi_1 \ldots \int\limits_{\varphi_{n-1}^{(0)}}^{\varphi_{n-1}^{(1)}} d\varphi_{n-1} \int\limits_0^R \varrho^{n-\beta-1} \cdot r^{\alpha-n}(y, I)\, d\varrho,$$

it then becomes clear that $q(K_R)$ is a continuous function of $\varphi_k^{(0)}$, $\varphi_k^{(1)}$, $k = 1, \ldots, n-1$.

Let us prove that $q(K_R)$ takes on different values. The function $\varrho^{-\beta}(y)$ is invariant under rotation of the cone but the function $r^{\alpha-n}(y, I)$ achieves a minimum on the negative part of the $0y_1$ axis and a maximum on the positive part.

Thus $q_k(R)$ is not a constant, continuous function of the angles which characterize its location. Hence,

$$\max q_k(R) = q_{K_0}(R), \quad \min q_k(R) = q_{K_1}(R), \quad q_{K_0}(R) > q_{K_1}(R),$$

where K_0, K_1 are some positions of the cone, are achieved. In the case of a "circular" cone, when φ_k^0, φ_k^1 are constants, K_0 is the position of K for which $I \in K$ and $0y_1$ is the axis of symmetry, and K_1 is the position of K when $I \bar{\in} K$ and the negative part of $0y_1$ is the axis of symmetry.

Let us consider the integral

$$q_m(R) = \int\limits_{III_R} \varrho_m^{-\beta}(y) r^{\alpha-n}(y, I)\, dy,$$

where $\varrho_m^2(y) = y_1^2 + \cdots + y_m^2$, $1 \leqq m \leqq n$, $0 < \alpha < \beta < m$. We have an integral with a singular manifold $\varrho_m(y) = 0$ and the singular point $y = I$. Since they are not combined, we may limit ourselves to the neighborhood $\varrho_m = 0$, where $r^{\alpha-n}(y, I) \leqq C$ in investigating the existence of the integral.

Transforming to multiple integrals, we have

$$q_m(R) \leqq C_1 \cdot \int\limits_{III_R} \varrho_m^{-\beta}(y)\, dy_1 \cdots dy_m.$$

Here $\varrho_m = 0$ is a singular point so that the integral converges for $\beta < m$ and diverges for $\beta \geqq m$.

Let us prove that Lemma 2.1 is valid for $q_m(R)$.

Following the proof of Lemma 2.1, let us transform again to polar coordinates. Taking into account that $\varrho_m = \varrho \cdot \psi(\sigma)$, where $\psi(\sigma)$ is some continuous function of σ, we obtain

$$q_m(R) = \int\limits_\sigma d\sigma \int\limits_0^R \frac{\psi(\sigma) \cdot \varrho^{n-\beta-1} d\varrho}{(\varrho^2 - 2\varrho \cos \varphi_1 + 1)^{\frac{n-\alpha}{2}}},$$

from which

$$q_m'(R) = R^{n-\beta-1} \int\limits_\sigma \frac{\psi(\sigma)\, d\sigma}{(R^2 - R \cos \varphi_1)^{\frac{n-2}{2}}}$$

and, furthermore, the whole reasoning is duplicated.

Integrals where the domains of integration will be the cones K_R are considered analogously.

2.2. On some Properties of the Integral $\int\limits_D r^{\alpha-n}(x, t) f(t)\, dt$.

Lemma 2.2. If $0 < \alpha < 1$, $f(t) \in S(\overline{D})$ and

$$v(x) = \int\limits_D \frac{f(t)\, dt}{r^{n-\alpha}(x, t)}, \qquad (2.4)$$

then $v \in H(\alpha)$ everywhere in the domain D, including its boundary.

Proof.

$$|\Delta_x v| = \int\limits_D \frac{|r^{n-\alpha}(x+\Delta x, t) - r^{n-\alpha}(x,t)|}{r^{n-\alpha}(x,t)\cdot r^{n-\alpha}(x+\Delta x, t)} \cdot |f(t)| \cdot dt \leqq \operatorname{Sup}_D |(f(x)|$$

$$\times \int\limits_D \frac{|r^{n-\alpha}(x+\Delta x, t) - r^{n-\alpha}(x,t)|}{r^{n-\alpha}(x,t)\, r^{n-\alpha}(x+\Delta x, t)} \cdot dt.$$

Let us transfer the origin to the point x, then $r(x, t) = \varrho(y)$, the domain D goes over into D_x, but $D_x < Ш(d)$, where $Ш(d)$ is a sphere of radius d, which is the diameter of the domain D. Thus

$$|\Delta_x v| \lesseqgtr \int\limits_{Ш(d)} \frac{|r^{n-\alpha}(\Delta x, y) - \varrho^{n-\alpha}(y)|}{\varrho^{n-\alpha}(y)\, r(\Delta x, y)} dy\, \|f\|_{S(D)}.$$

Now, let us rotate the coordinate axes so that the point Δx would lie on the $0y$ axis; then $\Delta x = (\Delta x_1, 0, \ldots, 0)$ so that

$$|\Delta_x v| \leqq \int\limits_{Ш(a)} \frac{|r^{n-\alpha}(\Delta x_1, y) - \varrho^{n-\alpha}(y)|}{\varrho^{n-\alpha}(y)\, r^{n-\alpha}(\Delta x_1, y)} dy \cdot \|f\|_{S(D)}.$$

The inversion $y_i = \Delta x_1 \cdot z_i$, $i = 1, \ldots, n$ yields:

$$\varrho(y) = |\Delta x_1| \cdot \varrho(z),$$

$$dy = |\Delta x_1|^n dz, \quad r^2(\Delta x_1, y) = (\Delta x_1 - y_1)^2 + \sum_2^n y_k^2$$

$$= |\Delta x_1|^2 \left[(z_1 - 1)^2 + \sum_2^n z_k^2\right]$$

i.e.,

$$r(\Delta x_1, y) = |\Delta x_1| \cdot r(z, y),$$

$$|\Delta_x v| \leqq \|f\|_{S(D)} \cdot \int\limits_{Ш\left(\frac{d}{|\Delta x_1|}\right)} \frac{r^{n-\alpha}(z, I)\, |\Delta x_1|^{n-\alpha} - \varrho^{n-\alpha}(z)\, |\Delta x_1|^{n-\alpha}}{|\Delta x_1|^{n-\alpha} \varrho^{n-\alpha}(z) \cdot r^{n-\alpha}(z, I)\, |\Delta x_1|^{n-\alpha}}$$

$$\times |\Delta x_1|^n dz = \|f\|_{S(D)} \frac{|\Delta x_1|^{n+n-\alpha}}{|\Delta x_1|^{2(n-\alpha)}} \int\limits_{Ш\left(\frac{d}{|\Delta x_1|}\right)} \frac{|r^{n-\alpha}(z, I) - \varrho^{n-\alpha}(z)|}{\varrho^{n-\alpha}(z) \cdot r^{n-\alpha}(z, I)} dz \leqq |\Delta x_1|^\alpha$$

$$\times C(\alpha, n)\, \|f\|_{S(D)},$$

that is

$$|\Delta_x v| \leqq C(\alpha, n) \, \|f\|_{S(D)} \cdot |\Delta x_1|^\alpha, \tag{2.5}$$

where

$$C(\alpha, n) = \int\limits_E \frac{|r^{n-\alpha}(z, I) - \varrho^{n-\alpha}(z)|}{r^{n-\alpha}(z, I) \cdot \varrho^{n-\alpha}(z)} \, dz. \tag{2.6}$$

Let us prove the existence of this integral. Let us transform the expression

$$\frac{|r^{n-\alpha}(z, I) - \varrho^{n-\alpha} z)|}{\varrho^{n-\alpha}(z)} = \frac{\left|\left[\varrho^2(z) - 2z + 1\right]^{\frac{n-\alpha}{2}} - \varrho^{n-\alpha}(z)\right|}{\varrho^{n-\alpha}(z)}$$

$$= \left|\left(1 - \frac{2z_1 - 1}{\varrho^2}\right)^{\frac{n-\alpha}{2}} - 1\right|.$$

where $\dfrac{2z_1 - 1}{\varrho^2} \to 0$ for $\varrho \to \infty$ and the inequality

$$\left(1 - \frac{2z - 1}{\varrho^2}\right)^{\frac{n-\alpha}{2}} - 1 < K \cdot \frac{|2z_1 - 1|}{\varrho^2} \leqq K_1 \cdot \frac{1}{\varrho}$$

is valid. Hence

$$C(\alpha, n) \leqq K_1 \int\limits_E \frac{dz}{\varrho(z) \cdot r^{n-\alpha}(z, I)}. \tag{2.7}$$

Since $0 < \alpha < 1$, then $1 + n - \alpha > n$, and the integral converges. The Lemma is proved.

Remark 1. It follows from the inequality (2.5) that (2.4) defines the linear operation from $S(D)$ into $H(\alpha)$ and is completely continuous from $S(D)$ into $C(D)$.

Integrals of the form (2.4), called integrals of potential type, have been studied by many authors, see [74] and [29]. However, what is apparently new here is the assertion: $v \in H(\alpha)$, $0 < \alpha < 1$. $V(x)$ has been studied for $\alpha \geqq 1$ in potential theory [25]. If $\alpha > 1$, then $V \in C^1$. For $\alpha = 1$ it may only be asserted that $v \in H(1 - \varepsilon)$ and $V \in C^1$ only for $f \in H$.

Remark 2. If $f(t) \in L_p^{(D)}$ and

$$\frac{n}{p} < \alpha < \frac{n}{p} + 1, \tag{2.8}$$

then by the same method, except involving the Hölder inequality, we obtain $V(x) \in H\left(\alpha - \frac{n}{p}\right)$, in which the operation (2.4) is again linear and completely continuous from $L_p(D)$ into $C(D)$. The assertion on the linearity and complete continuity is valid under just the condition $\alpha > \frac{n}{p}$ and the result is not new, see [72] page 362, or [29] page 336. The second condition [2.8] bounds the Hölder exponent.

2.3. Properties of the Simplest Singular Function $\omega(x)$. Let us examine the function

$$\omega(R, x) \equiv \omega(Ш_R, x) = \varrho^{\beta-\alpha}(x) \cdot \int\limits_{Ш_R} \varrho^{\beta}(t) \cdot r^{\alpha-n}(x, t)\, dt \tag{2.9}$$

We shall often omit the mention of the domain and shall simply write $\omega(x)$.

By rotating the coordinate system we may direct the $0t_1$ axis through the point x then

$$x = (x_1, 0, \ldots, 0), \qquad r^2(x, t) = (x_1 - t_1)^2 + \sum_{i=2}^{n} t_i^2,$$

$\varrho(t)$ and the sphere $Ш_R$ do not change and the Jacobian of the transformation equals ± 1. Hence, it is seen that $\omega(R, x)$ depends only on $\varrho(x)$. Let us now put $t_i = \varrho(x) \cdot y_i$, $i = 1, \ldots, n$, then

$$\varrho(t) = \varrho(x) \cdot \varrho(y),$$

$$dt = \varrho^n(x) \cdot dy,$$

$$r^2(x, t) = (x_1 - \varrho(x) \cdot y_1)^2 + \varrho^2(x) \cdot \sum_{i=2}^{n} y_i^2$$

$$= \varrho^2(x)\left[\left(\frac{x_1}{(\varrho x)} - y_1\right)^2 + \sum_{i=2}^{n} y_i^2\right] = \varrho^2(x) \cdot r^2(y, I_x),$$

where $I_x\left(\frac{x_1}{\varrho(x)}, 0 \ldots, 0\right)$ is a point of the unit hypersphere. The sphere III_R is hence transformed into the sphere $III\left(\frac{R}{\varrho(x)}\right)$. Thus

$$\omega(R, x) = \varrho^{\beta-\alpha}(x) \cdot \int\limits_{III\left(\frac{R}{\varrho(x)}\right)} \frac{\varrho^n(x) \cdot dy}{\varrho^{n-\alpha}(x) r^{n-\alpha}(y, I_x) \varrho^\beta(x) \cdot \varrho^\beta(y)}$$

$$= \int\limits_{III\left(\frac{R}{\varrho(x)}\right)} \varrho^{-\beta}(y) \cdot r^{\alpha-n}(y, I_x) \cdot dy.$$

Since the integral must depend only on $\varrho(x)$, we may then take any fixed point on the surface of the unit hypersphere, $I(1, 0, \ldots, 0)$ say, in place of I_x so that

$$\omega(R, x) = q\left(\frac{R}{\varrho(x)}, \alpha, \beta\right) \equiv q\left(\frac{R}{\varrho(x)}\right), \tag{2.10}$$

where the function q is given by (2.1). Hence, we have for $R \to \infty$

$$\varrho^{\beta-\alpha}(x) \cdot \int\limits_E \varrho^{-\beta}(t) r^{\alpha-n}(x, t)\, dt = q(\alpha, \beta), \tag{2.11}$$

where $q(\alpha, \beta)$ is given by (2.2).

It follows from the properties of the function q that $\omega(x)$ is a monotonely decreasing function of $\varrho(x)$ in the whole space $0 \leqq \varrho \leqq \infty$, $\omega(0) = q$, $\omega(\infty) = 0$ and $\omega(x) \in H(\lambda)$, where $\lambda = \min(\alpha, \beta - a, n - \beta, 1)$.

More exactly, $\omega(\varrho) \in H(\gamma)$, $\gamma = \max(\alpha, 1)$ for all $\varrho \neq 0, \infty, R$ and $\omega(\varrho) \in H(\lambda)$ where $\lambda = \beta - \alpha$ for $\varrho = 0$, $\lambda = n - \beta$ for $\varrho = \infty$ and $\lambda = \alpha$ for $\varrho = R$.

Now, let us consider the function

$$\omega(D, x) = \varrho^{\beta-\alpha}(x) \cdot \int\limits_D \varrho^{-\beta}(t) r^{\alpha-n}(x, t)\, dt,$$

with an arbitrary domain of integration.

Since 0 is an inner point of the domain D, then numbers $a, R > 0$ (we do not exclude $R = \infty$) are found such that $III_a < D < III_R$ and

$$\omega(III_a, x) \leqq \omega(D, x) \leqq \omega(III_R, x),$$

which according to (2.10) yields

$$q\left(\frac{a}{\varrho(x)}\right) \leqq \omega(D, x) \leqq q\left(\frac{R}{\varrho(x)}\right). \tag{2.12}$$

Since $q\left(\frac{a}{\varrho}\right)$, $q\left(\frac{R}{\varrho}\right) \to q$ as $\varrho \to 0$, then $\omega(0) = q$ and

$$q\left(\frac{a}{\varrho}\right) - q \leqq \omega(x) - \omega(0) \leqq q\left(\frac{R}{\varrho}\right) - q.$$

Hence, it is seen that $\omega(x)$ increases as $x \to 0$ and since $q\left(\frac{a}{\varrho}\right)$, $q\left(\frac{R}{\varrho}\right) \in H(\beta - \alpha)$ at the point $\varrho = 0$ and $\in H(n - \beta)$ for $\varrho = \infty$, then $\omega(x)$ satisfies the Hölder condition with exponent $\beta - \alpha$ at the point 0 and with exponent $n - \beta$ at $x = \infty$.

2.4. Case of a Singular Boundary Point. Now let 0 be a boundary point of the domain D. If the point M were to run over the boundary Γ of the domain D, the ray $0M$ would describe some surface. We designate the maximum portion of the space which it bounds and which contains D, as the cone of visibility V of the domain D from the point 0. The family of rays tangent to Γ at 0 generates a tangent cone K. Evidently, always $K < V$. If the domain D is convex, then $K = V$, if 0 is a point of smoothness, then K is a half-space, etc. In general, we do not exclude cases when 0 is a smoothness point of the surface and K may degenerate into a manifold of lesser dimension, mes $K = 0$, or conversely, may coincide with all of space. Rotating the coordinate axes such that the $0t_1$ axis would pass through the point x, and performing a similarity transformation with center at 0 and radius $\frac{1}{|x_1|} = \frac{1}{\varrho(x)}$, we obtain

$$\omega(D, x) = \int_{D_x} \varrho^{-\beta}(y) r^{\alpha-n}(y, I)\, dy,$$

where D_x is the domain obtained from D by means of the two mentioned transformations. In the one-dimensional case $(n = 1)$ rotation is superfluous.

We denote the point of intersection of the ray $0x$ with the unit sphere by $\theta(x)$, $\theta(x) = (\theta_1(x), \ldots, \theta_{n-2}(x))$, where $\theta_k(x) = (\widehat{0x_k, 0x})$. Then it may be said that the domain D_x has been obtained from D "by a rotation" through the angle $\theta(x)$ and an "extension" of $\dfrac{1}{\varrho(x)}$ times.

Let D first be a cone K. Then $D_x = K_{\theta(x)}$ and $\omega(K\,x), = q(K_{\theta(x)})$, where $K_{\theta(x)}$ is the cone K, rotated through the angle θ, $\theta(x)$ varies within the opening of K. If $\varrho(x) \to 0$ along the ray $\theta(x) = \theta$, then

$$\lim_{\substack{\varrho(x)\to 0\\ \theta(x)=0}} \omega(K, x) = q(K_\theta).$$

Since $q(K_\theta)$ takes on different values depending on θ (see section 2 of part 1), $\omega(K, x)$ is discontinuous at the point $x = 0$ and its values occupy the segment $[q(K_1), q(K_0)]$, where K_1 and K_0 are the minimum and maximum positions of the cone K_θ.

If $D = K\sigma$ is a truncated cone, we obtain analogously

$$D_x = K\left(\theta(x), \frac{\sigma}{\varrho(x)}\right) \quad \text{and} \quad \lim_{\substack{\varrho(x)\to 0\\ \theta(x)=0}} \omega(K\sigma, x) = q(K_\theta).$$

Let us majorize the domain D on two sides by the truncated cones $\tilde{K}_a$ and V_R, where V_R is the cone of visibility of the domain D from the point 0, and we may consider the opening of $\tilde{K}_a$ to tend to the opening of the cone of tangents as $a \to 0$. Thus

$$\tilde{K}_a < D < V_R,\ \tilde{K}\left(\theta_x, \frac{a}{\varrho(x)}\right) < D_x < V\left(\theta(x), \frac{R}{\varrho(x)}\right)$$

and

$$q\left(\tilde{K}_\theta, \frac{a}{\varrho(x)}\right) \leqq \omega(D, x) \leqq q\left(V_\theta, \frac{R}{\varrho(x)}\right). \tag{2.13}$$

There exist positions $\tilde{K}_1$ and V_0, such that

$$\min_\theta q\left(\tilde{K}_\theta, \frac{a}{\varrho(x)}\right) = q\left(\tilde{K}_1, \frac{a}{\varrho}\right), \quad \max_\theta q\left(V_\theta \frac{R}{\varrho}\right) = q\left(V_0, \left(\frac{R}{\varrho}\right)\right),$$

so that

$$q\left(\tilde{K}_1, \frac{a}{\varrho(x)}\right) \leqq \omega(D, x) \leqq q\left(V_0, \frac{R}{\varrho(x)}\right). \tag{2.14}$$

Let us elucidate the behavior of $\omega(D, x)$ at the point $x = 0$. Isolating the small circle $D_a = D \cap Ш_a$ and partitioning the domain $D = D_a + (D - D_a)$, we arrive at the investigation of $\omega(D_a, x)$, because $\omega(D - D_a, x) \in C^\infty$ at the point $x = 0$.
For the domain D_a the cone of visibility of V_a and $\tilde{K}_a$ is close to K_a, where $K_a = K \cap Ш_a$. Applying inequality (2.13), we have

$$q\left(\tilde{K}_\theta, \frac{a}{\varrho(x)}\right) \leqq \omega(D_a, x) \leqq q\left(\tilde{V}_\theta, \frac{a}{\varrho(x)}\right),$$

from which we obtain

$$q(\tilde{K}_\theta) \leqq \lim_{\substack{\varrho(x)\to 0 \\ \Theta(x)=\Theta}} \omega(D_a, x) \leqq q(V_\theta).$$

Selecting a small a, we may consider $q(K_\theta)$ and $q(V_\theta)$ sufficiently similar. On the other hand, the values of $q(K_\theta)$ and $q(V_\theta)$ for different θ fill some segments. Hence it is clear that $\omega(D_a, x)$ has different limits along the rays, i.e., is discontinuous at the point $x = 0$.
Summarizing the investigations of the preceding paragraphs, we obtain the following theorem:

Theorem 2.1. Let 0 be an inner point of the finite domain D. Then the function

$$\omega(x) = \omega(D, x) = \varrho^{\beta-\alpha}(x) \cdot \int_D \varrho^{-\beta}(t) \cdot r^{\alpha-n}(x, t)\, dt$$

is continuous in the whole space and satisfies the Hölder condition with exponent λ, where $\lambda = \beta - \alpha$ for the point 0; for the rest of the domain D, including the boundary, $\lambda = \alpha$ for $\alpha < 1$, $\lambda = 1 - \varepsilon$ for $\alpha = 1$ and $\omega(x) \in C^1(D)$ for $\alpha > 1$; $\lambda = n - \beta$ for $x = \infty$ and $\omega(x) \in C^\infty$ outside D. Moreover, the inequalities

$$q\left(\frac{a}{\varrho, x}\right) \leqq \omega(x) \leqq q\left(\frac{R}{\varrho(x)}\right),$$

are valid, where a and R are the minimum and maximum radii of the domain D from the point 0; it hence follows that

$$\max \omega(x) = \omega(0) = q(\alpha, \beta), \qquad \min \omega(x) = \omega(\infty) = 0.$$

If 0 is a boundary point of the domain with nondegenerate cone of tangents and $n \geqq 2$, then in contrast to the preceding, $\omega(x)$ is discontinuous at the point 0 (has different limits along the rays). $\omega(x)$ has no discontinuity for $n = 1$ and has the same properties at the boundary point as at the inner points.

2.5. Generalization to an Infinite Domain. For unbounded domains it is necessary to add that the point ∞ also plays the part of a singular point for them and all the facts mentioned above for finite singular points also hold for the infinitely distant point.

Let us first consider the case when there is just one singularity ∞, that is the point 0 does not belong to the domain. In other words, let an arbitrary unbounded domain D_∞ be given and let $0 \,\bar{\in}\, D_\infty$. Performing the inversion

$$x_i = \frac{\xi_i}{\varrho^2(\xi)}, \quad \varrho(x) \cdot \varrho(\xi) = 1,$$

we convert the domain D_∞ into the finite domain D_*, whereupon the point ∞ goes over into the point 0. Let us designate the point ∞ as an inner or boundary point for D_∞ if the point 0 is, respectively, an inner or boundary point of the domain D_*. In the case of a boundary point it is also possible to introduce the concept of the cone of tangents and the cone of visibility of the domain D_∞ from the point ∞.

Let ∞ be an inner point of D_∞. We may then construct spheres $Ш_\alpha$, $Ш_R$, such that $Ш_R^- < D_\infty < Ш_\alpha^-$ and, correspondingly,

$$\int_{Ш_R^-} \leqq \int_{D_\infty} \leqq \int_{Ш_a^-}$$

or

$$\varrho^{\beta-\alpha} \int_{Ш_R^-} \leqq \varrho^{\beta-\alpha} \int_{D_\infty} \leqq \varrho^{\beta-\alpha} \int_{Ш_a^-}$$

or

$$\omega(Ш_R^-, x) \leqq \omega(D_\infty, x) \leqq \omega(Ш_a^-, x).$$

Since

$$\int_{III_R} = \int_E - \int_{III_R}, \qquad \int_{III_a} = \int_E - \int_{III_a}$$

$$\int_E = q, \quad \int_{III_R} = q\left(\frac{R}{\varrho(x)}\right), \quad \int_{III_a} = q\left(\frac{a}{\varrho(x)}\right),$$

we then have

$$q - q\left(\frac{R}{\varrho(x)}\right) \leqq \omega(D_\infty, x) \leqq q - q\left(\frac{a}{\varrho(x)}\right).$$

Taking into account the properties of the functions $q\left(\frac{a}{\varrho}\right)$ and $q\left(\frac{R}{\varrho}\right)$, we obtain for the function $\omega(D_\infty, x) \equiv \omega(x) : \omega(x)$ achieves its maximum $\omega(\infty) = q$ at its singular point $x = \infty$, and $\omega(x) \in H(n - \beta)$, it achieves the minimum $\omega(0) = 0$ and $\omega(x) \in H(\beta - \alpha)$ at $x = 0$. Completely analogously to the preceding, we investigate the case when ∞ is a boundary point. Hence, we see that the point $x = \infty$ plays the same part for the integrals of the kind under consideration as does the point 0.

2.6. Case of Several Singular Points. Now let there be several singular points $c_1, c_2, \ldots, c_i$, part of which lie within the domain D, and part on the boundary. If the domain D is not bounded, then another point $c_{i+1} = \infty$ is appended to the singular points. Let us first consider the case of a finite domain. Let

$$\omega(D, \Pi, x) = \Pi^{\beta-\alpha}(x) \cdot \int_D \frac{dt}{\Pi^\beta(t) \cdot r^{n-\alpha}(x, t)}.$$

As is easy to see, the domain D is divided into parts D_i such that $c_i \in D_i$ and $\Pi(x) = \Pi_i(x)$ on D_i, where $\Pi_i(x) = r(x, c_i)$.
Let us use the notation

$$\omega_i(x) = \Pi_i^{\beta-\alpha}(x) \int_{Di} \frac{dt}{\Pi_i^\beta(t) \cdot r^{n-\alpha}(x, t)}.$$

If c_i is an interior point of D_i, then $\omega_i(x)$ is continuous at this point $\omega(x) \in H(\beta - \alpha)$ and

$$q\left(K_i, \frac{a_i}{\Pi_i(x)}\right) \leqq \omega_i(x) \leqq q\left(V_i, \frac{R_i}{\Pi_i(x)}\right),$$

where K_i and V_i are cones constructed for the domain D_i exactly as has been mentioned above, where $K_i = V_i = E$ for the interior points. Because $\int\limits_D = \sum\limits_1^l \int\limits_{D_i}$, we obtain:

$$\text{for } x \in D_i \qquad \omega(D, \Pi, x) = \Pi_i^{\beta-\alpha}(x) \int\limits_D \geqq \Pi_i^{\beta-\alpha}(x) \int\limits_{D_i} = \omega_i(x),$$

i.e., $\omega(D, \Pi, x) \geqq \omega_i(x)$, $i = 1, l$ in D_i. On the other hand

$$\omega(D, \Pi, x) = \Pi^{\beta-\alpha}(x) \cdot \sum_{i=1}^{l} \int\limits_{D_i} \frac{dt}{\Pi_i^{\beta-\alpha}(t) \cdot r^{n-\alpha}(x, t)}$$

$$= \Pi^{\beta-\alpha}(x) \sum_1^l \frac{1}{\Pi_i^{\beta-\alpha}(x)} \omega_i(x) \leqq \sum_{i=1}^{l} \omega_i(x),$$

since $\Pi(x) \leqq \Pi_i(x)$ for all $i = 1, \ldots, l$. Thus

$$\omega(D, \Pi, x) \geqq \omega_i(x) \quad \text{in} \quad D_i \tag{2.15}$$

and for all $x \in D$

$$\omega(D, \Pi, x) \leqq \sum_1^l \omega_j(x), \tag{2.16}$$

or

$$q\left(K_i, \frac{a_j}{\Pi_i(x)}\right) \leqq \omega(D, \Pi, x) \leqq \sum_{j=1}^{i} q\left(V_j, \frac{R_j}{\Pi_j(x)}\right), \qquad i = 1, l, \tag{2.17}$$

where a_j, R_j are the radii of the spheres inscribed within and circumscribed about D_j.

Let us use the notation

$$B = \operatorname*{Sup}_{x \in D} \sum_{i=1}^{l} \frac{1}{\Pi_i^{\beta-\alpha}(x)} \Pi^{\beta-\alpha}(x) = \operatorname*{Sup}_{x \in D} \sum_{i=1}^{l} \left(\frac{\Pi(x)}{\Pi_i(x)}\right)^{\beta-\alpha} \tag{2.18}$$

Since $\lim\limits_{x\to c_i}\dfrac{\Pi(x)}{\Pi_i(x)} = 1$, and similarly as $x \to \infty$, the quantity B is then finite even if the domain D is not bounded.

Using the notation $h_\Pi = \operatorname*{Sup}\limits_{D} \omega(D, \Pi, x)$ and $h_i = \operatorname*{Sup}\limits_{D_i} \omega_i(x)$, we then have $h_i \leqq h_\Pi \leqq B \cdot \max q(V_i)$ and because of (2.17) we may write

$$\max_{1\leqq i\leqq l} q(K_i) \leqq h_\Pi \leqq B \cdot \max_{1\leqq j\leqq l} q(V_j). \tag{2.19}$$

If the domain D is unbounded, by cutting part of it off with a sphere of sufficiently large radius we will obtain a finite domain containing all the singular points $c_1, c_2, \ldots, c_l$ and another domain D_{l+1}, containing only the singular point $c_{l+1} = \infty$. Duplicating all the computations again for this case, we obtain the inequalities (2.14), (2.15) and (2.19), where i runs through values from 1 to $l+1$ and K_{l+1}, V_{l+1} are the tangent and visibility cones of the domain D from the point $c_{l+1} = \infty$.

3. Integrals with Singular Manifolds

3.1. Singular Manifolds. Let us introduce the notation

$$r_m^2(x, t) = \sum_{i=1}^{m} (x_i - t_i)^2, \text{ such that } r_n \equiv r, r_1 = |x_1 - t_1|,$$

$$\varrho_m^2(x) = r_m^2(x, 0) = \sum_1^m x_i^2.$$

E_{n-m} is the coordinate hyperplane $x_1 = 0, \ldots, x_m = 0$, also described by the condition $\varrho_m(x) = 0$.

E_m is the coordinate hyperplane $x_{m+1} = \cdots = x_n = 0$.

We shall write the volume element in these spaces as dv_{n-m} and dv_m

$$Ш(E_m, R) \text{ is the sphere } \sum_1^m x_k^2 \leqq R^2 \text{ in } E_m.$$

We shall use the sign $\times$ of the topological product in order to write $E = E_m \times E_{n-m}$, say. The domain $Ц = Ш(E_m, R) \times E_{n-m}$ is called a cylinder (circular and infinite). Let be given an arbitrary, bounded or unbounded, simply- or multiply-connected, n-dimensional domain D with boundary Γ.

Let us consider the integral

$$\omega_m(D, x) = \varrho_m^{\beta-\alpha}(x) \cdot \int_D \varrho_m^{-\beta}(t) r^{\alpha-n}(x, t)\, dt, \tag{3.1}$$

where α and β are two arbitrary numbers subject to the inequalities $0 < \alpha < \beta < m$; m is an integer, and $1 \leqq m < n$. In addition to the moving singular point $t = x$ the integrand has the fixed singularity $\varrho_m(t) = 0$, i.e., the coordinate hyperplane E_{n-m}. We consider that E_{n-m} either intersects or is tangent to the domain D. Let us denote their common portion by F. If D and E_{n-m} intersect, the singular manifold F is of dimension $n - m$. If E_{n-m} is tangent to D, then F may have a smaller dimensionality, but we would then consider another subspace E_{n-m}. Hence, we may consider that the dimensionality of F is $n - m$ even in this case. When $m = n F$ consists of individual points, this case has been studied above and we eliminate it. When $m = 1$ F will have the same dimensionality $n - 1$, as the surface Γ.

Because of the positivity of the integrand, the integral (3.1) exists together with any of the multiple integrals.

If the integral with respect to $dt_1 \cdots dt_m = dv_m$ is separated out, $\varrho_m(t) = 0$ will be its singular point so that the integral exists for $\beta < m$ but not for $\beta \geqq m$.

3.2. Three Lemmas

Lemma 3.1. If $\beta > 1$ and $y \neq 0$, then

$$\int_{-\infty}^{\infty} \frac{ds}{\left(s^2 + y^2\right)^{\frac{\beta}{2}}} = \frac{\varkappa}{|y|^{\beta-1}}, \tag{3.2}$$

where

$$\varkappa \equiv \varkappa(\beta) = \sqrt{\pi} \cdot \frac{\Gamma\left(\frac{\beta-1}{2}\right)}{\Gamma\left(\frac{\beta}{2}\right)}. \tag{3.3}$$